Whoppers!

Scripts and Poems for Reading Aloud

compiled by John Foster

Oxford University Press

Oxford University Press, Walton Street, Oxford OX2 6 DP

Oxford New York Toronto
Delhi Bombay Calcutta Madras Karachi
Kuala Lumpur Singapore Hong Kong Tokyo
Nairobi Dar es Salaam Cape Town
Melbourne Auckland Madrid

and associate companies in
Berlin Ibadan

Oxford is a trade mark of Oxford University Press

Published by Oxford University Press 1992
Reprinted 1993

A CIP catalogue record for this book is available from the British Library.

ISBN 0 19 916552 1

Typeset by Pentacor PLC, High Wycombe
Printed and bound in Hong Kong

Contents

Whoppers

Eric Finney

A poem for two voices

'I'm having a pony for Christmas,
And a meal at a posh hotel.'
*'That's nothing, I'm having video,
And two colour tellies as well.'*

'My dad's having a Rolls Royce car.'
*'Well, my dad's having two –
One for his window-cleaning gear
And one for Mum – brand new.'*

'My mum's having a baby.'
*'Well, my mum's having twins –
Or maybe she'll have triplets,
Or even quads or quins.'*

'I'm having a sailing dinghy:
Cor, won't the neighbours go green!'
'*We're having the yacht Britannia
Bought secondhand from the Queen.*'

'We're off to the Costa Brava,
Dad's getting tickets quite soon.'
'*I'll think of you then while we're on
Our luxury tour of the moon.*'

. . . .

'To tell you the truth, I've been fibbing
And boasting, I realize.'
'*That's nothing: I've not been telling fibs,
But monstrous, walloping lies!*'

Camping Out

Judith Nicholls

A poem for three voices and an owl

Can we sleep out in the tent, Dad?
Go on, just him and me!
It's a full moon,
not a cloud in sight!
We'll be quiet as
mice when the cat's about –
oh, *please* let us stay the night?

You can pitch your tent down the garden
by the lilac, or just behind;
but mind you're in by midnight
if you're going to change your mind.
The key will be out till twelve,
but not a second more.
I don't want prowlers after that –
at twelve I lock the door!

Great, Dad!
We'll be out till morning –
you've never let us before!
We'll fetch all we need
before it's dark
then you can lock the door.

The key will be out till twelve,
I said, but not a second more!

Now, what do we need?
Water, jug,
toothpaste, mug,
towel, rug,
toothbrush . . .

Since when were you so keen
on keeping clean?

You can't camp out down the Amazon
without the proper gear.
We could be here a *year*,
exploring dark Brazil
until – who knows?

All right, a torch then,
I suppose. Sleeping bags.
Pillows?

There's no room.
Mosquito nets come first,
and books to read
by torch or moon.
Pencils, notebooks.
Sweaters – two at least.
And don't forget the midnight feast!

What do explorers eat?
Will crisps and apples do,
with peanut-butter sandwiches,
bananas, orange juice,
and baked beans for the stew?

They'll do!

I wish we'd brought a pillow.
It's really dark.
I thought you said no cloud?
Should we close the flap –
to keep mosquitoes out, I mean?

Or leopards!

. . . and to keep us warm.
There goes that flash again.
The air feels heavy.
P'rhaps a jungle storm?
Listen!
Can you hear – a breeze?
Something's rustling,
quickly, *freeze!*

Could it be
some deadly snake,
uncoiling for . . .

For goodness sake,
it's only trees!

Oh, look!
What IS that shadow up above?
I'm sure I saw it move!

It's nothing,
just the lilac.
Or some bat or owl
out on the prowl
for supper too.

Toowhit, Toowhoo!

No need to jump,
it's nearer me than you!

I didn't jump!
What time is it,
only five to midnight?
Just wondered.
Thought it might be more.

I don't want prowlers after that,
at twelve I LOCK THE DOOR . . . !

Aren't you cold?
I wish we'd brought more blankets,
the jungle's not so hot
when sun's gone down;
we didn't think of that.

Not cold, just hungry.
It's great out here,
but as for food –
we should have brought much more.
Explorers need their sustenance.
Another time, we'll plan it better . . .

But meantime,

Race you to the door!

Dialogue of the Deaf

Jerome Fletcher

A poem for two voices

Monday

I don't know why he bothers.
He never listens to what I say.
Without taking his nose out of his paper, he'll ask:
'So what did you do today?'
'So, Sam, what did you do today, son?'

There! What did I tell you!

'Well, Dad, let me see . . .
I killed a fire-breathing dragon,
And rescued a damsel in distress,
Who turned out to be the postman,
Wearing a pink chiffon dress.
I fought most of the night with a monster,
About the size of Loch Ness.
The garden was swimming in blood by dawn . . .'

'I hope you cleared up the mess,
And didn't leave any bits on the lawn.
I don't work all weekend in that garden
Just for you to untidy it again.'

'No, Dad.'

Tuesday

'So what did you do today, Sam?'

'Well, Dad, let me see . . .
Oh yes! Me and my friend, Andy,
Started World War Three!
We began by invading Portugal.
(That was just before tea.)
Then later on, in an armoured car,
We devastated the USSR . . . '

*'I hope you tell your mother where you are,
And don't go off on your own?
And I think he's a bad influence on you, that boy Andy!'*

'Yes, Dad.'

Wednesday

'Well, son, what did you get up to, today?'

'Ummmmm, now what did I do?
I locked Granny and Granpa in the coalhouse,
And cousin Alice in the loo.
I buried Uncle Walter,
Though he wasn't entirely dead.
Tomorrow I'm running away from home . . . '

*'I think it's time for bed.
You've had a long day today, Sam,
And you need your sleep.'*

Why do I bother, eh?

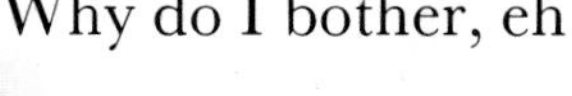

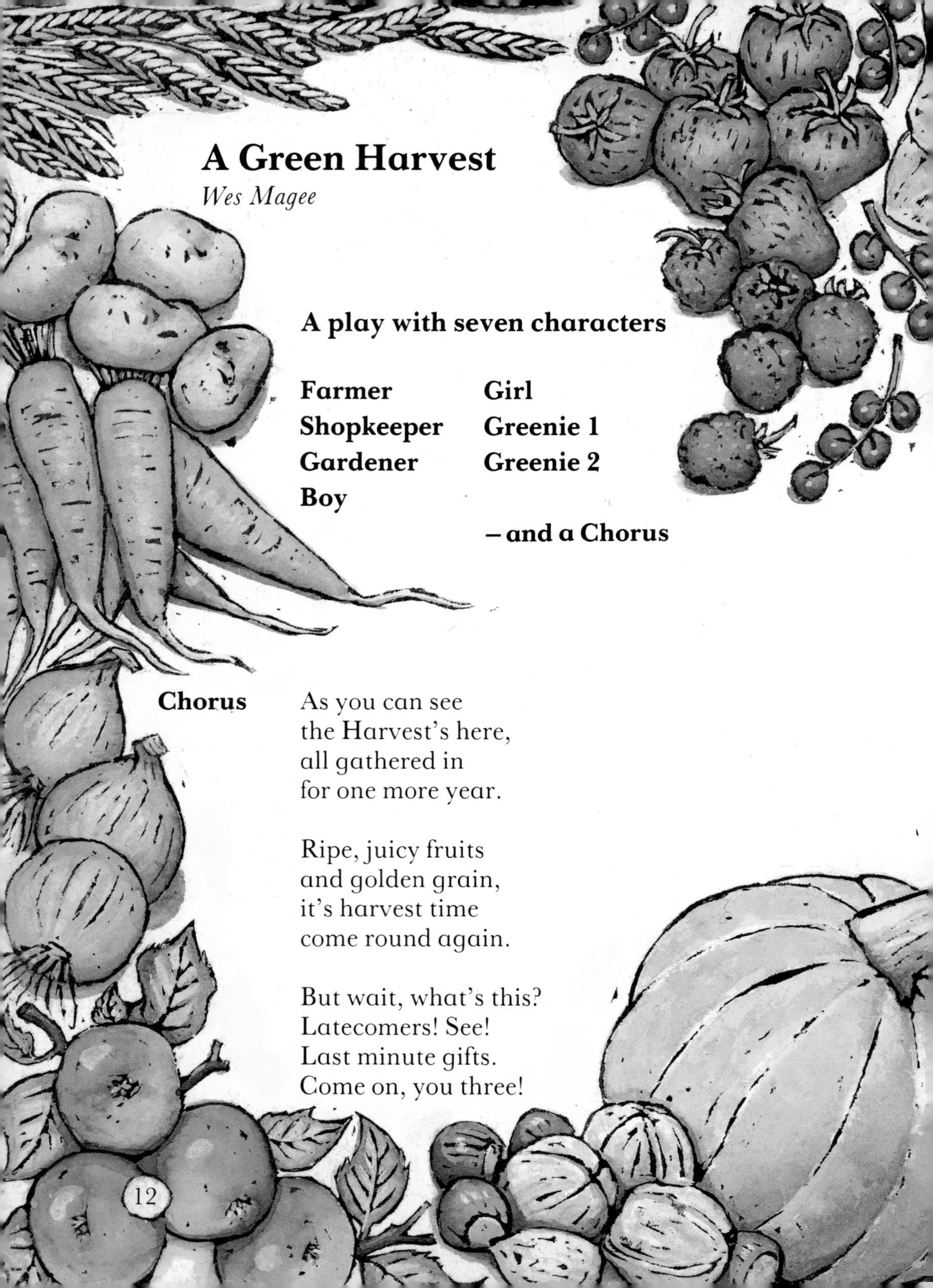

A Green Harvest

Wes Magee

A play with seven characters

Farmer	**Girl**
Shopkeeper	**Greenie 1**
Gardener	**Greenie 2**
Boy	

– and a Chorus

Chorus As you can see
the Harvest's here,
all gathered in
for one more year.

Ripe, juicy fruits
and golden grain,
it's harvest time
come round again.

But wait, what's this?
Latecomers! See!
Last minute gifts.
Come on, you three!

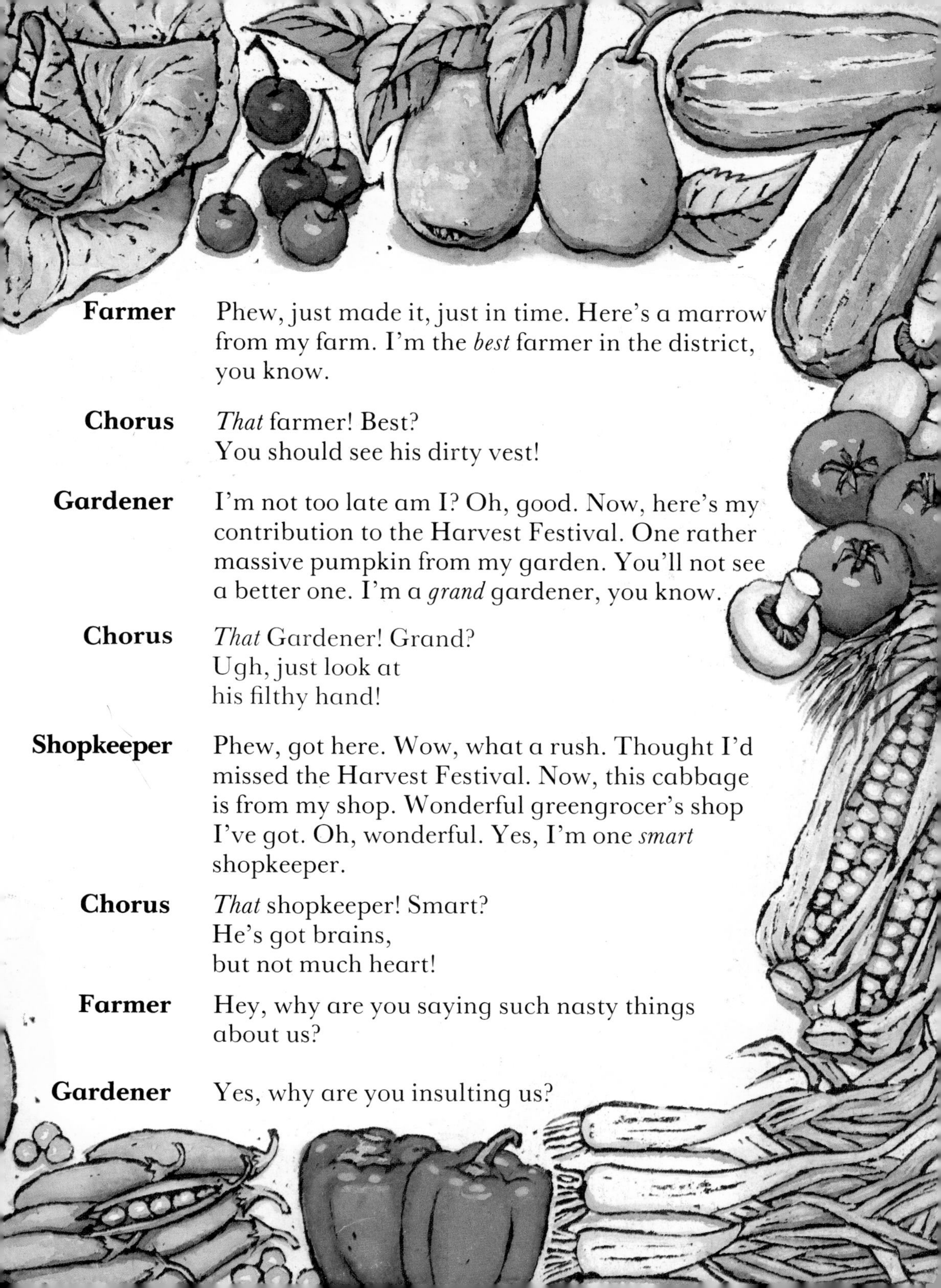

Farmer Phew, just made it, just in time. Here's a marrow from my farm. I'm the *best* farmer in the district, you know.

Chorus *That* farmer! Best?
You should see his dirty vest!

Gardener I'm not too late am I? Oh, good. Now, here's my contribution to the Harvest Festival. One rather massive pumpkin from my garden. You'll not see a better one. I'm a *grand* gardener, you know.

Chorus *That* Gardener! Grand?
Ugh, just look at
his filthy hand!

Shopkeeper Phew, got here. Wow, what a rush. Thought I'd missed the Harvest Festival. Now, this cabbage is from my shop. Wonderful greengrocer's shop I've got. Oh, wonderful. Yes, I'm one *smart* shopkeeper.

Chorus *That* shopkeeper! Smart?
He's got brains,
but not much heart!

Farmer Hey, why are you saying such nasty things about us?

Gardener Yes, why are you insulting us?

Shopkeeper We've brought food for your Harvest Festival. You should be jolly grateful.

Chorus Oh, we are, we are,
we're grateful, you know.
But just think
what happened an hour ago.

Farmer Happened?

Gardener An hour ago?

Shopkeeper Nothing happened. Come on, they're talking nonsense . . . and it's rhyming nonsense, which is even worse!

Chorus Wait a minute,
have no fear.
A flashback
will make all clear.

Farmer
Gardener Flashback?
Shopkeeper

Chorus Flashback!!

(Flashback effect.)

Chorus We're back one hour.
Now look, and see
what you were up to.
One! Two! Three!

Farmer Now the harvest's gathered in I've got bags of left-over fertilizer.
Got to get rid of it somewhere.
But where? I know, I'll chuck it *in the river!*
Here goes.

Gardener I've got tons of rotting rubbish from my garden.
Phew, it's vile. Where can I dump it?
Ah, *the river* will wash it all away. Here goes!

Shopkeeper I've got piles of junk in my shop. Wooden boxes, cardboard boxes, plastic bags. I'll just dump them here on the *river bank!* No problem. Here goes!

Chorus Look at these three,
dumping their junk.
They chuck it away
and do a bunk!

(Farmer, Gardener and Shopkeeper try to run away.)

Chorus Hold it! Stop! STOP!

Farmer Stop?

Gardener Us?

Shopkeeper What for?

Chorus Dumping rubbish! Polluting the river!
Just you listen to this.

(Enter boy and girl.)

Boy Hey, look at the river. Look at that awful rubbish floating in the water.

Girl Look, dead fish. All the chemicals and rubbish must have killed them.

Boy And here's a dead bird.

Girl This is terrible. The river's ruined, ruined.

Chorus *(Pointing to Farmer, Gardener and Shopkeeper)*

See what you've done,
You rotten meanies.
We'll have to call in
the clean-up Greenies!

(Enter the Greenies.)

Greenie 1	Oh boy, have we got a job here.
Greenie 2	We'll soon get it all cleaned up.
Boy	But the fish are dead.
Girl	And the birds are dead.
Boy	There's rubbish!
Girl	There's litter!
Greenie 1	Well, we'll have to use our special powers to clean up the place.
Greenie 2	And then the birds and fish can live again.
Boy	But how?
Girl	Yes, how?
Greenie 1	We need the Water Cleaners to help us. Water Cleaners!

(Water Cleaners enter and dance.)

Greenie 2 And we need the Land Cleaners to help us. Land Cleaners!

(Land Cleaners enter and dance.)

Greenie 1 And we need the Air Cleaners to help us. Air Cleaners!

(Air Cleaners enter and dance.)

Chorus A magic touch,
and the river's clean.
So try and keep
our wide world green.

Farmer I never thought . . .

Gardener Neither did I . . .

Shopkeeper I feel ashamed . . .

Chorus Well, that's time past,
one hour ago.
Now let's get back
to our Harvest show!

(Flash effect.)

Farmer All this marvellous display of food from our planet, and *we* were polluting the river and the land.

Chorus You've learned the lesson.
Keep our planet clean.
Let's have rivers blue
and fields of green.

But now you see
our Harvest here,
all gathered in
for one more year.

Ripe, juicy fruits
and golden grain,
it's harvest time
come round again.

Leave Me Alone

David Williams

A play with six characters

Rani	**Meg**
Kate	**Mrs Burns**
Sharon	**Mrs Patel**

At school

(The bell rings.)

Mrs Burns Move out quietly, children. Rani, would you stay behind for a moment, please?

Rani Yes, Mrs Burns?

Mrs Burns Rani, where has your nice smile gone?

Rani Nowhere.

Mrs Burns Are you sad about something?

Rani No.

Mrs Burns You will tell me, won't you, if there is anything wrong?

Rani Yes, Mrs Burns.

(Outside the classroom door.)

Kate What did she want?

Rani Nothing much.

Kate Did she tell you off?

Rani What about?

Kate You got your sums wrong.

Rani She didn't talk about them.

Kate What did she say?

Rani Nothing. Leave me alone.

Kate Can't I walk home with you?

Rani No. Leave me alone.

(She runs off.)

At home

(The TV is on. Rani's mother is in another room.)

Mrs Patel Rani. Have you seen my bag?

(She comes in.)

Have you seen my bag?

Rani No.

Mrs Patel Here it is beside you, silly. Now how did that get there?

Rani You must have left it there.

Mrs Patel No. Oh, well. Look, it's lovely outside. Don't you want to play with your friends?

Rani I'm watching this.

Mrs Patel The news?

Rani I'm watching it!

Mrs Patel All right. Don't bite my head off. What's got into you, girl?

Rani Leave me alone.

In the playground

Sharon Have you got it?

Rani Yes. Will you leave me alone now, please?

Meg Maybe.

Sharon Maybe not.

Rani Please.

Meg Here's her friend coming.

Sharon We'll see you later.

(*Meg and Sharon run off*)

Kate Rani! I've been looking for you.

Rani Why?

Kate To play. Who were those big girls?

Rani I don't know.

Kate You were talking to them. You gave them something.

Rani I didn't.

Kate I saw you, Rani.

Rani Please don't say anything. I'll be in big trouble.

Kate Who with? Those girls?

Rani Ssh. Don't say anything. Don't tell.

Kate Are we still friends?

Rani Yes. If you don't tell.

Kate I won't. I promise.

At home

(The doorbell rings. Mrs Patel opens the door.)

Kate Hello, Mrs Patel. Is Rani in?

Mrs Patel No. She went out. I thought she must be with you.

Kate I haven't seen her.

Mrs Patel Come in. I want to talk to you. You sit with Rani at school, don't you?

Kate Yes.

Mrs Patel How is she doing at school? Is she working hard?

Kate Well . . .

Mrs Patel Is Mrs Burns happy with her?

Kate She likes Rani a lot.

Mrs Patel My girl has always been good at school. She learned to read very quickly.

Kate She's very good.

Mrs Patel But now I have a note from Mrs Burns. She wants to see me about Rani. Do you know why?

Kate No, Mrs Patel.

Mrs Patel I told Rani what was in the note. But she didn't want to talk about it. She went out.

Kate I'll go and look for her.

Mrs Patel Wait. I want you to tell me. Has Rani been buying a lot of sweets lately? Or other things?

Kate No. Why?

Mrs Patel She's such a good girl. But something is wrong just now. Kate, you are her best friend, aren't you?

Kate Yes, I think so.

Mrs Patel And you would tell me if something was wrong?

Kate Well, yes.

Mrs Patel I want to tell you something. Some money is missing from my purse.

Kate Have you lost it?

Mrs Patel I think maybe Rani took it.

Kate She wouldn't do that!

Mrs Patel She has never done anything like this before. But I think it is her. It has happened twice now.

Kate Have you asked Rani?

Mrs Patel She won't let me talk to her just now. What is wrong with her?

Kate I don't know.

Mrs Patel Please talk to her for me. Tell her it doesn't matter about the money. But I want her to talk to me.

Kate Yes, Mrs Patel. I'll go and find her.

In the street

(It is raining. Rani is standing in a dark corner.)

Kate Is that you, Rani?

Rani Leave me alone.

Kate What are you doing here? Your mum wants you.

Rani I don't want to see her. I'm going to be in trouble.

Kate No. She told me . . .

Rani Look. There's Meg and Sharon. Hide.

Kate Why?

Rani I'm scared of them. They won't leave me alone.

Meg There she is.

Sharon Come here, you.

Kate Go away. She doesn't want to play.

Sharon We wouldn't play with *her*.

Kate Why do you want her, then?

Meg She owes us some money.

Kate She doesn't.

Sharon Shut up.

Meg Have you got the money?

Rani It's here. That's all I can get.

Meg You'll have to get more tomorrow.

Sharon And you, what's your name?

Kate Kate.

Sharon You'd better shut up about it or you'll get this.

(She shows her fist.)

Right?

Meg Come on, Sharon. I'm getting wet.

(Meg and Sharon leave.)

Kate You'll have to tell your mum about this.

Rani I'm scared to. They'll get me if I do. You *must* keep it a secret. Do you promise?

Kate Will you go back home if I do?

Rani Yes.

Kate I promise.

In school

(Kate knocks on the classroom door.)

Mrs Burns Come in. Hello, Kate. You're early.

Kate Mrs Burns, can I talk to you?

Mrs Burns Of course.

Kate Rani is my best friend.

Mrs Burns I know.

Kate And I promised her I would keep a secret.

Mrs Burns Is it the secret that is making her unhappy?

Kate Yes.

Mrs Burns If you're her best friend you should tell someone who can help.

Kate Even if I've promised not to?

Mrs Burns You should do what you think is right.

Kate I think it's right to tell.

Mrs Burns Do you want to tell me?

Kate Yes. Rani is scared.

Mrs Burns What of?

Kate Two big girls. Meg and Sharon.

Mrs Burns I know them.

Kate They are making Rani give them money.

Mrs Burns What money?

Kate Her mum's. Rani is taking it for the girls. If she won't, they're going to hit her.

Mrs Burns I see. Is she scared to tell her mum?

Kate Yes.

Mrs Burns You were right to tell me, Kate. No one should keep bad secrets.

Kate I'm scared of the girls too.

Mrs Burns Don't worry. Nothing will happen to you or Rani. I promise.

In the playground

Rani Kate.

Kate Hello, Rani.

Rani My mum went to see Mrs Burns. She knows about Meg and Sharon.

Kate Is it all right?

Rani Yes. They've given Mum all her money back. I saw them too.

Kate Were you scared?

Rani No. They cried and they said they were really sorry. They won't harm us any more.

Kate Rani, *I* told Mrs Burns about them. I broke my promise.

Rani It doesn't matter. I'm glad you did.

Kate It's nice to see you smile again.

Rani It feels nice.

Kate Come on. Let's show Mrs Burns.

Rani I'll race you.

Kate No. Let's go in together.

Rani Okay.

(They run off, hand in hand)

Acknowledgements

The editor and publisher are grateful for permission to include the following material:

Eric Finney, 'Whoppers', first published in *Another Third Poetry Book* (Oxford University Press). © Eric Finney. Reprinted by permission of the author. Thanks are also due to the author for permission to use the title of his poem as the volume title. Jerome Fletcher, 'Dialogue of the Deaf', from *A Gerbil in the Hoover*, published by Doubleday. © Jerome Fletcher 1989. All rights reserved. Wes Magee, 'A Green Harvest', © Wes Magee 1992. Reprinted by permission of the author. Judith Nicholls, 'Camping Out', from *Dragonsfire* (Faber & Faber Ltd), © Judith Nicholls 1990. Reprinted by permission. David Williams, 'Leave Me Alone', © David Williams 1992. Reprinted by permission of the author.

Illustrations are by: Bucket pp. 4–5; Ann Johns pp. 6–9; Bill Piggins pp. 10–11; Judy Stevens pp. 12–19; Ann Strugnell pp. 20–31.